# Green Spaces in City Places

Cars honk. A motorcycle zips by. People scurry around town like busy ants. City life can get pretty hectic. Sometimes you need a place to relax. Luckily, there are plenty of green spaces in the city. Just head to your nearest city park with your family. You can find lots to do.

A city park has many spots to rest, play, and learn. **63** You can sit on a bench and read a book or feed the pigeons. Maybe a friend will meet you at the playground for some afternoon fun. Perhaps you can hike to a nature center or fly a kite.

All sorts of people visit city parks each day of the week. After all, everyone needs a bit of green space now and then. Don't you?

# City Park, USA

⭐ **G**irls play basketball. A dad pushes his baby in a stroller. A couple jogs along a trail with two dogs. These are some things you might see at your city park. Look around. What else do you see?

38 Each city park is different. Some parks have swings, slides, and sandboxes. Other parks have swimming pools and tennis courts. Some may have jogging trails or horseback riding. At some parks, you can even bring a tent and camp out overnight!

79 Some city parks are located next to rivers or lakes. At these parks, you might find people swimming or boating. A city park in a mountain area has places for people to go rock climbing or hiking.

116 All city parks have one thing in common though. They are full of smiling faces. Maybe yours is one of them.

# Dad's Concert in the Park

⭐ **"W**ait for me!" yelled Emma. Her younger brother Michael ran toward a big oak tree.

⭐ "How about right here?" asked Michael. Emma nodded. Their mother spread out a big blanket on the ground. People began to fill the city park for the afternoon concert.

⭐ "I hope Dad can see us," said Michael. "The park is starting to get crowded."

⭐ "Don't worry," said Emma. "Remember what Dad told us this morning. The concert won't start until he knows we are here."

⭐ The musicians took their seats. The conductor looked out at the crowd of people. "There's Dad," yelled Michael. "Hello, Dad! Look over here!" Michael tried to shout over the noisy crowd. "I don't think he can hear me," Michael said sadly.

⭐ Just then, the conductor waved his arms in the air. The musicians began to play. "See, Michael? Dad started the concert for us," said Emma. "He must have heard you after all." Michael smiled and gave Emma a big hug. It sure was fun to watch Dad conduct a concert in the park.

# A Trail of Park Helpers

**M**ia and Santos grabbed their colored chalk and sat at their assigned spots by the sidewalk. "Artists, get ready!" shouted a city park worker. "Ready, set, doodle!" Mia and Santos giggled as they began to draw their picture. Chalk It Up Day was their favorite city park event.

Hundreds of children showed up each year. This year was no different. Santos picked up a blue piece of chalk. "Now remember," he said, "our sidewalk picture has to show park helpers."

"We can draw Mr. Jacobsen," said Mia. "He helps out at the city park pool."

"What about Kate's mom?" asked Santos. "She runs the city park summer camp. We can draw her, too."

 "Let's get busy," said Mia. The two friends worked until they had finished their chalk art picture.

"I think that's it," Santos said at last. "I can't think of any more park helpers. Can you?"

"No, I guess we're finished," said Mia. Just then a trail of ants marched across the sidewalk. Each one carried a small piece of food. "Look, ants!" called Mia. "I guess they want to help keep the park clean."

Santos laughed. "I think our trail of park helpers wants to be in our picture," he said. "Let's help them out." Santos gave Mia a piece of chalk, and they busily finished their picture.

# Park Police

**P**ark police have lots to do. They patrol city parks. They must keep things running smoothly. Some city park officers drive cars. Others prefer to walk or ride bicycles. Some even ride horses. It doesn't matter how they get around though. They are always there to keep us safe. ㊾

You may think that park police are new. Yet George Washington formed the park police in 1791. Park police have kept us safe for more than 200 years. They make sure park rules and laws are followed. Park police have been doing their jobs for a long, long time.

# Seeing Stars

⭐ **"I**t's movie time!" shouted Derek. "Race you to the van!" He picked up his goggles and sprinted past Anna.

19 Anna had no idea what Derek was talking about. She knew they were going to Sunset Pool at Midview City Park. Anna climbed into the van and sat next to Derek.

50 "Ready for the movie?" asked Dad.

56 "What are you talking about?" Anna asked. "I thought we were going swimming."

69 "Don't you remember?" asked Derek. "It's Flick and Float Night at the pool. Everyone watches a movie and floats on the water."

91 Anna looked up at the night sky and chuckled. "Gee, I can't wait to tell my friends that I saw stars at the movies!"

# Let's Get Moving

"Closed for repairs," said Quincy, staring at the sign by the train. "I can't believe it. Old Red's been here forever."

"I know," said Kayla. "I rode on Old Red for the first time when I was a baby." Kayla followed Quincy up the path to the visitor's center. They found out that the train needed a new engine, but the park was low on funds.

**66** "I've got an idea," said Quincy. Soon Kayla and Quincy finished their signs at the city art center. Then, they found a big jar and wrote "Save Old Red" across the front.

"Let's stand by Old Red to collect money," said Kayla.

"Good idea," said Quincy. "We'd better get moving so Old Red can, too!"

# A Park for All Seasons

**A**s seasons change, so do events that happen in city parks. Meet a friend at the fall festival. You can listen to music, play games, and buy crafts. Take along a snack and watch a Thanksgiving play. Could there be a part in the play for you?

Walk through the park in the crisp, autumn air. Maybe you'll collect a colorful leaf or two. You can string acorns to make a necklace. Be sure to bring your camera!

Does winter snow dot the landscape where you live? If so, building a snowman in the park is lots of fun. Perhaps it's too cold or rainy outside. A trip to the city park art center is a great way to spend the day. You can cut out paper snowflakes or make a calendar. Maybe you'll just listen to a story and draw a picture. Afterward, you can sip hot chocolate. Yummy!

# Wild Things in the Park

★**A**re you a nature lover? Spring and summer are perfect seasons to sign up for a city park nature walk. Pack up a hand lens and a camera. You might want to take along a notebook, too.

★The nature tour leader speaks to your group. "Don't chase the wild things. Let them come to you." You jot down what she says along with several new facts.

★As you walk along the dirt path that winds through the park, the leader points out many of the park's occupants. Look! It's a robin—the first sign of spring. You notice an endangered falcon resting in the treetops, and you snap a picture. Bees buzz around wildflowers in full bloom. A lizard basks on a large rock.

★There are all sorts of interesting plants, but don't touch that one! It has three leaves. Suddenly you remember something you wrote down earlier. "Leaves of three, let them be." Oh no, poison ivy! That's one wild thing you don't want to encounter.

# A Living Part of History

**H**ave you ever been to Philadelphia? It has one of the largest city parks in the world. It's a chain of parks called Fairmount Park. The park is just minutes away from any part of the city.

Fairmount Park is home to more than 1 million trees. People can walk, skate, or ride their bikes along miles of paths. (59)

Fairmount Park is a living part of history, too. Just look around. You can stop at one of its 200 statues. Many nearby buildings are more than 100 years old.

What else can you find? You can see the oldest zoo in our country. Fairmount Park is a fun place to learn about our past!

# Northern Lights

It looks like lights dancing in the sky or an amazing fireworks display. The night sky lights up in red, green, blue, and violet streaks of light. What is this crazy light show? It's called the Northern Lights. The Northern Lights can be seen from countries in the far north. They appear mostly in the sky in the Arctic region.

In Finland, a story says that an Arctic fox started fires with its tail. They call the lights "fox fires."

**80** The real story is that the sun causes the Northern Lights. The sun gives off energy bits. These bits form a cloud, which moves like a stream. This cloud is called the solar wind. The solar wind flows to Earth and bumps into gases around the Earth. This causes a glow. That beautiful glow is the Northern Lights.

# A Roar in the Woods

⭐**Q**uinn stepped out of his cousin's van and looked around. He'd never been out of the city. All the hikers put on their backpacks and headed down the trail.

**29** The first thing Quinn noticed was the quiet. Then, he listened more closely. There were the sounds of crunching sticks and leaves under hiking boots, birds chirping high in the trees, and his lunch rustling in his backpack.

**67** Slowly, the trail turned and got steeper. Quinn heard a new, faint sound. The trail turned again, and suddenly the faint sound became a roar. Was there a subway, a train, or a big truck out here in the woods?

**107** Quinn looked and listened more closely. At the top of the hill, Quinn and his cousin stopped. The roar was so loud they had to shout over the sound. All that noise came from water. It flowed over rocks and became white and foamy.

⭐Quinn discovered the cause of the roar. It was the roar of a waterfall.

# The Grand Canyon

⭐**S**uppose you wanted to walk to the bottom of the Grand Canyon. You would have to walk for one whole day just to get to the river at the bottom of the canyon. That's walking just to the bottom, not to the bottom and back up! It is almost a mile straight down from the top of the canyon to the bottom. But the trail doesn't go straight down. It winds and curves around. It's a long hike!

⭐The walls of the Grand Canyon are layers of rock. Each layer has its own color. These layers of colors give the Grand Canyon much of its beauty.

⭐The Colorado River has flowed through the rock for millions of years. Each year, it wears away more of the rock. This wearing away of the rock formed the canyon. The canyon grows bigger and bigger.

⭐Most people visit the south rim of the canyon. It is easy to get around by car or walking. There are hotels, roads, and overlooks on the south rim.

⭐The north rim of the canyon is the wild side. It is far from any towns and doesn't have many roads. In winter, it snows more on the north rim. The north rim is closed to visitors part of the year because of weather.

⭐The Grand Canyon is one of nature's wonders. The canyon is so huge and so beautiful that it is hard to imagine.

# Roy G. Biv

**W**ho is Roy G. Biv? Each letter in that name stands for the first letter in a color. That's red, orange, yellow, green, blue, indigo, and violet. Those seven colors are the colors in a rainbow.

Why do you always see a rainbow around rain? Sunlight is made up of colors. When the sunlight shines through water, like a raindrop, it shows its many colors.

Where is the sun when you look at a rainbow? The sun is always behind you when you are looking at a rainbow. You'll see the rain in the rainbow side of the sky.

Let's get back to Roy G. Biv. Roy's name tells the rainbow's colors. It also tells the order the colors are seen in a rainbow. Red is on the outside. It is followed by orange, yellow, green, blue, and indigo. Violet is on the inside.

Sometimes two rainbows appear. This is called a double rainbow. The colors in the second rainbow are the opposite. Violet is on the outside of the second rainbow. Red is on the inside. The second rainbow is lighter in color than the first.

The next time you see a rainbow, check to see if Roy G. Biv is there.

# Team Colors

**M**adison's favorite coach was Ms. Acosta. Madison wanted to give Ms. Acosta a gift, but she didn't have any money. Madison sat with her head in her hands. She twirled her necklace on her finger. Then, she had an idea.

Madison stirred salt, flour, and water. She cooked the mixture until it was thick. Then, she rolled the dough into little balls. She used a toothpick to make a hole through the middle of each ball to make beads. Then, she baked the beads in the oven. ⑧⑦

Madison spread newspapers outside. She waited for the beads to cool. She painted half the beads green and half the beads gold. Madison placed a gold bead on a string. Then, she added a green bead. She filled the string with gold and green beads. Finally, she tied the string in a knot. Madison had made a necklace for Ms. Acosta in the team colors of green and gold.

# World's Largest Flower

The Titan Arum is called the "world's largest flower." It is often called something else, though. Some people call it "Mr. Stinky."

The Titan was first found in Indonesia. It has one large leaf shaped like an umbrella. But this is not a leaf you would see growing in most gardens. It can grow to be 20 feet high and 15 feet across. The stem of the leaf is as big as a person's thigh! But, the leaf is not the most interesting part of the plant. It's the flower of the Titan that gets all the attention.

98 The Titan has only one flower. What an amazing flower it is. The flower is more than 7 feet tall. That's taller than most grown men! The flower only lasts two to three days. It's not a flower anyone would want to sniff though. The flower of the Titan Arum lets off a strong odor. The smell has been described as "rotting fish with burnt sugar." The stinking odor lasts about eight hours.

# Beauty at the Beach

⭐ **"H**ave you ever seen a photograph of the Earth taken from space?" asked Aunt Cammy. "You see that the Earth is mostly blue because most of the Earth is water. The mighty oceans cover a large part of the Earth."

**40** "I'd like to see the ocean," Keith said. "Can we go?"

**51** Aunt Cammy said, "Great idea! Let's take a 'beauty walk' at the beach. We'll stop and look at things we find beautiful. Too many times we just walk right by."

**81** Keith ran to get his bathing suit.

**88** When they got to the beach, Aunt Cammy said, "Isn't the white sand beautiful? It is smooth and sparkles in the sun like diamonds."

**112** Keith and Aunt Cammy walked along the ocean's edge. Keith stopped and gazed at a seashell that was the color of the moon.

**135** Aunt Cammy pointed to a starfish. Keith bent down. Suddenly, a wave washed it away! Aunt Cammy grabbed Keith's arm so he wouldn't wash away, too.

**161** They played in the surf, sat in the sun, walked, and looked. They talked about each beautiful thing they found. They didn't pick anything up. They left them for someone else to enjoy.

**194** On the ride home, Keith said, "The ocean is full of life and full of surprises. I noticed many things today. It is fun to walk slowly and look hard. Maybe tomorrow we can walk around the neighborhood and look for beautiful things."

**237** Aunt Cammy nodded and said, "There is beauty and wonder all around us!"

# Volcano!

⭐ **V**olcanoes are made when melted rock inside the Earth grows. The hot rock fills holes under the ground. When the rocks on the surface can no longer hold the hot rock below, the volcano blows. Fire shoots up. Smoke comes out. Hot rock flows down the mountain. It covers everything in its path. It is dangerous and beautiful.

⭐ A live volcano is an amazing thing to see. Few people in the United States have seen one. Yet, there are 50 live volcanoes in this country.

⭐ Most of these volcanoes are in Alaska. There are 40 volcanoes on islands in Alaska. These are far from people. One or two of them erupt each year.

⭐ Most volcanoes are near the Pacific Ocean. Some are under the sea. Hawaii has many live volcanoes. Hot rock quietly flows from them.

⭐ In 1980, a volcano erupted in Washington. That volcano was Mount St. Helens. Very hot rocks, gas, and smoke filled the air. It was so hot that snow and ice melted. Ash filled the sky. When it was over, the mountain was bigger.

# The Legend of the Bluebonnet

**L**ong ago, in the land of the Comanche, it was very dry. It had not rained in a long, long time. Dancers danced in hopes of making it rain. No rains came.

One girl, She-Who-Is-Alone, watched the dancers and held her doll. Her doll wore beads and blue feathers in her hair. She-Who-Is-Alone loved her doll. She carried it with her everywhere.

Wise Man called the people together. He said that the Great Spirits were not happy. He said that people were not sharing. They were taking things from the Earth but not giving anything back. He said that the people should choose an object that is important to them. They should burn it. They should scatter the ashes to the winds. After this happens, the rains will come.

The people wondered what they should give up. Someone thought it should be a bow. One person said it should be a special blanket.

★ She-Who-Is-Alone thought about her doll. It was the most important thing to her. She knew what she must do.

Everyone went to bed. She-Who-Is-Alone got up. She took her doll and walked up a hill.

"Great Spirits," she said. "Here is my special doll. It is the most important thing to me. I want you to have it." Then she made a fire and put her doll in it. After the fire went out, She-Who-Is-Alone scooped up the ashes. She scattered them to the winds.

She lay down and cried herself to sleep. The sun's morning rays touched She-Who-Is-Alone's face. She woke and looked at the hills. The ground was covered with blue flowers. The flowers were the same blue color as the feather from her doll's hair.

Now, every spring She-Who-Is-Alone is remembered when bluebonnets cover the hills in Texas.

# Where the Buffalo Roam

**D**o you know the song "Home on the Range"? The words are "Oh, give me a home where the buffalo roam." It would be hard to find that home today. Once, there were 60 million buffalo on the Great Plains. They covered the plains as far as the eye could see.

Buffalo were important to the Plains Indians. They used them for food. They used the hides for clothing. They also used the hides to make their houses. They only killed the ones they needed. ⑧⑤

Then, hunters came. In just 40 years, hunters killed almost all of the buffalo. They were hunted for their hides. Buffalo robes were sold in cities and across the ocean in Europe. By 1893, there were 300 buffalo left.

In 1905, laws saved the buffalo. Today, they are no longer endangered. There are now more than 80,000 in America.

# A Gecko's Tale

★**I**f a gecko could talk, it might tell you an amazing tale. What's the story? Why, it's about a tail—a gecko's tail.

²³ A gecko is a kind of lizard. Geckos live in warm places such as rain forests, deserts, grasslands, and marshes. Many people also keep them as pets.

⁵⁰ Geckos come in all sizes. Some kinds arc only the length of your fingernail. Others are longer than your foot.

⁷⁰ Geckos hunt for food at night. They move quickly and silently, so they can catch crickets and roaches. Sometimes they eat small birds and mice.

⁹⁵ A gecko has a short, thick tail. Its tail helps it survive. What happens when another animal catches a gecko?

¹¹⁵ The gecko lets go of its tail and escapes! Later, it grows a new one. Now that's an amazing but true tale!

# Waiting to Bloom

**I**n April 2003, people at the Beardsley Zoo saw an unusual sight. This zoo in Connecticut is home to an 80-year-old mother of pups. An animal, you ask? No, not at all. It's an 80-year-old plant. It makes young plants called "pups."

This desert plant is called a century plant. It takes a long time for the plant to bloom. Most don't take 100 years, though. The century plant uses all of its energy to bloom. It blooms only one time. Then, it dies.

[88] This century plant was given to the zoo in 1956. One day in 2003, a zoo worker noticed something. A flower spike had started to grow from the 4-foot plant. Soon, the spike grew 25 feet in the air.

In April, yellow and green flowers had bloomed, and the plant had lived its full life. Don't worry, though. New pups are ready to take its place.

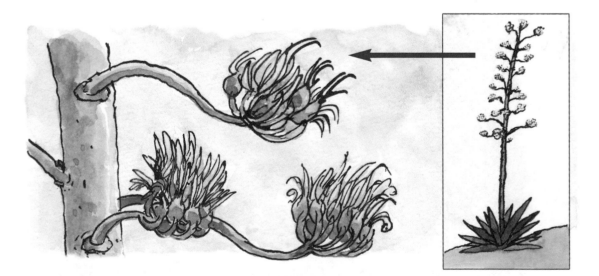

# Saving the Penguins

"The penguins will fly in soon," said Dad. "Get ready." It sounded strange. Penguins don't fly. Still, I knew what Dad meant. The penguins were being flown here to Cape Town. We were waiting to help them.

Back home in the United States, Dad works as a veterinarian. Sometimes I help keep the animals calm. That's why Dad brought me with him to South Africa.

Two weeks ago, a ship sank off the coast of South Africa, causing a terrible oil spill. The oil spread across the water to a nearby island where thousands of African penguins nested. The adult penguins and their chicks were in danger. Some say this spill was the worst ever.

"Elisabeth, come over here," called Dad. I followed him to the penguin pools. "You'll work here with Dr. Uribe," said Dad. "You can carry buckets of water and clean the small pools when they get too oily."

I couldn't wait to begin. Those poor penguins—I knew they needed our help. The penguins could die, unless we cleaned the oil from their feathers. Experts say it will take about three weeks for the oil spill to be cleaned up. The penguins can return home once their habitat is safe.

Suddenly, we heard an engine roar. I looked up and saw a plane. "They're here!" I yelled. Dad and the others unloaded large boxes with holes in the top. Inside were the frightened, oil-covered penguins.

I grabbed a bucket. I knew we had a long, busy day ahead of us. It would be hard work, but I knew that we could save the penguins.

# My Penguin Summer

"**H**ere you are, Elisabeth," said Dr. Uribe. "I believe you're ready." After just three days, I had become a penguin washer. I walked into the washing room. I held a toothbrush and a pair of gloves.

At first, I was a bit nervous. Then, I remembered what Dad had told me earlier. "Just treat them like the animals back home. Keep the penguins calm and handle them gently."

I put on my gloves. Then, I was paired with a girl named Kali. "Washing a penguin is a two-person job," she told me. I quickly learned that washing a penguin takes about 30 minutes. If a penguin is covered with lots of oil, it takes much longer, though.

First, the handler picks up a penguin from a pen and carries it to the washing room. Then, the handler puts it in a little tub of warm water. He or she tries to keep the penguin calm so it won't bite or die of shock.

As the washer, it was my job to clean the oil from its body. I used a special soap. First, I picked up a toothbrush. Then, I used it to gently clean the sticky oil from the penguin's face and head. I used my hands to wash its body. Luckily, the gloves kept the oil off of me!

The doctors gave each penguin vitamins to help it survive. In about three weeks, the penguins were ready. Their feathers were waterproof again. They were ready to swim back to their island. I'll never forget June of 2000. I'll always remember it as my penguin summer.

# Living in the Dark Zone

**T**here are some creatures most people have never seen. These creatures never see you, either. They live in the dark zone. The dark zone isn't a place in outer space. It's the area deep within a cave.

This cool, dark zone is home to all sorts of animals. Sunlight never reaches the dark zone. Many of these animals cannot see, such as the blind crayfish. Yet this is not a problem. Animals that live here must use other senses to stay alive.

⑧²Some dark zone animals have no eyes. The Texas Blind Salamander is one example. The Texas Blind Salamander has two small black dots under its skin where eyes would be found. It hunts in cave water for tiny snails and shrimp.

How can it find food if it can't see? It hunts for food in a special way. A snail or shrimp makes small waves when it moves in the water. The salamander can feel where the waves come from. Then, it knows that dinner is close by. Watch out, snail!

# Prairie Dog Town

**P**rairie dogs are not what they seem to be. Sure, they live on the prairie, but they are not dogs at all! A prairie dog is really a type of ground squirrel. Prairie dogs live in the western part of the United States and Mexico.

Prairie dogs prefer to live in large groups. These groups are made up of burrows, called towns. Prairie dogs search for food in the day and return to their burrows to sleep at night. [79] They mostly eat grass, seeds, leaves, flowers, and fruit. Sometimes prairie dogs will eat an occasional insect or two.

Many prairie animals like to hunt prairie dogs. What does a prairie dog do when a wolf, fox, or bobcat sneaks up on it ready to pounce? Zip! The prairie dog scrambles into its burrow. Whew! That was a close one!

# A Desert Monster

★ **C**asey woke up with a start. "What's that noise?"

⁹ Jonica rubbed her eyes and sat up in the tent. "What noise?" she asked. Then, she heard it, too.

²⁸ They grabbed a flashlight and climbed out of the tent, careful not to wake their parents.

⁴⁴ "The desert is home to all sorts of creatures," said Casey. "I sure hope we don't find one."

⁶² "You're letting your imagination run wild," Jonica replied, clinging to Casey's shirt.

⁷⁴ They crept along the path near the campsite. *Whooo!* Casey aimed the flashlight at the sound.

⁹⁰ "Look!" yelled Jonica. "It's a monster with two huge arms! It has gigantic eyes and a mouth!"

¹⁰⁷ The girls dashed back to the tent and hid under the covers. When day broke, they cautiously climbed out of the tent. "Maybe the monster's gone," said Jonica.

¹³⁵ They walked along the path. Then, Casey let out a loud laugh.

¹⁴⁷ The girls stood before a huge saguaro cactus. Its branches looked like arms. Three woodpecker holes formed two eyes and a mouth. Inside the "mouth" was a tiny owl.

¹⁷⁶ "Look at our desert monster now!" said Casey with a laugh.

# Father Goose

★ Just about everyone has heard the name Mother Goose. But, not many people know about a real man called Father Goose. Father Goose is the nickname of Bill Lishman. In 1994, Bill led 18 Canada geese south for the winter.

★ Bill Lishman was a metal sculptor and an inventor. He and his family lived in Canada. Bill loved animals and flying. One day, he and his family saw a film called *Skyward*. It showed geese that followed a boat. "I wonder if geese would follow a plane?" he asked himself. He asked an animal trainer for help.

★ Bill knew that some birds were in danger of losing their habitat. So, Bill decided to help them. He wanted to try first with Canada geese. The geese were not in danger, though. If Bill could teach the geese, he knew he'd be able to help birds that were at risk.

★ Bill kept many geese eggs on his farm. He watched them every day and waited for them to hatch. When geese hatch, they follow the first thing they see. This is called imprinting. Bill wanted the geese to imprint on him. Then, they would follow and learn from him, as if he were their parent.

★ The big day arrived! The geese hatched from their eggs. Bill was right there watching. He put the baby birds under heat lamps to stay warm. When they were strong enough, Bill taught them how to chase after him.

★ One day, Bill climbed into his small ultralight plane and drove around. The geese chased after Bill and his plane. A few days later, Bill flew the plane in the air. When he looked behind him he saw an incredible sight. The geese were flying after him!

# Fly Away Home

**B**ill could hardly believe it! His plan had worked. The geese followed behind him as he flew the ultralight. But, were the geese up for their big task? Could Bill teach them to fly south for the winter? These geese did not know how. They did not grow up in the wild. Winters in Canada were harsh and cold. If the geese did not fly south, they could die.

Each day, Bill flew the plane, and the geese flew behind him. Bill made sure that each trip was longer than the one before it. He wanted the geese to build up their strength to fly south in the fall. He knew their migration to Virginia would be a long one. Would they be able to make it?

On a crisp, autumn day in 1994, Bill knew he'd find out. Bill "Father Goose" Lishman and 18 Canada geese began their flight from Canada to Virginia. Bill hoped the geese would make it to their warm habitat.

⭐ Not only did the geese arrive safely, they remembered their migration path. By the following spring, the geese had returned to Canada. Bill's plan was a success! Now he could begin his work with birds that were in danger of losing their habitats. He could teach them to migrate to new places. Then, they would be safe.

Since then, Bill and others have formed Operation Migration. Bill has led other types of birds to safe places. Now these birds are growing in number.

You may think that Bill's work seems like something that happens in a movie. You are right. In 1996, a movie was made about Bill and his geese. It was called *Fly Away Home*. A movie always comes to an end though. Luckily, Bill's work with birds does not end. Thanks to Father Goose, birds in danger now have a chance to fly away home!

# Danger, Rattlesnakes!

**N**ick always played tricks on Tran. "I think it's time I teach Nick a lesson," said Tran. He gathered his things and sat down at the table. "A little bit of his own medicine should do the trick," said Tran. Then, he began to work.

First, Tran straightened a large paper clip. Next, he bent it into a wide *U*. Then, he pulled the rubber band through two holes in a button. He stretched the rubber band around both ends of the paper clip. ⑧④ Then, Tran wrote across the front of an envelope in big bold letters. It read: *Danger, Rattlesnakes!* He carefully flipped the button over dozens of times. Now the rubber band was twisted very tightly. Tran placed the whole thing inside the envelope. Then, he hid behind the sofa and waited for Nick.

Nick walked into the room and read the words aloud. "Danger, Rattlesnakes!" Nick said. He peeked inside the envelope and the button let loose. It rattled against the paper clip. "Aaahhhh!" yelled Nick. That sure was a lesson he'd never forget!

# We Need Trees

Trees and forests play an important role in life on Earth. Trees help hold soil in place, so it doesn't wash away. Trees give off oxygen, which people, plants, and animals need. Trees are also homes for many animals.

People cut down trees for many reasons. Sometimes they cut down trees to make room for houses and other buildings. Trees also are cut down so that farmers have room to plant their crops. Sometimes trees are cut down to be made into lumber or paper.

**85** Think about how life would be without trees. Cutting forests can change the weather. After rain falls in a forest, mist forms. This mist rises and becomes clouds. The clouds make rain. When the forests are cut down, no mist forms. The area grows drier because the rain cycle does not happen.

Cutting down forests also means that there are no trees to hold the soil. Rain washes the soil away, and the land is no longer good for plants.

Many countries are working to save forests. They are planting trees faster than they are being cut down. Recycling paper also helps. Fewer trees are cut down if new paper does not need to be made.

# One Man's Idea

Gaylord Nelson was worried about the Earth. It was 1963. He looked around and saw that the Earth was dirty. Many plants and animals were dying. He wondered how these problems could be solved. He talked to the president. He talked to other people who make laws. He wanted to do more.

[52] In 1969, Nelson had an idea. He thought that there could a special day called "Earth Day." On that day, people could try to solve the problems with the Earth's air, water, and land. He wrote letters to colleges telling about his idea. He wrote about his idea in a school magazine.

[104] Nelson's idea caught on. April 22, 1970, was the first Earth Day. People rode bikes, took the bus, or walked instead of using cars. They learned about problems with plants and animals. They learned about dirty air and water. People thought of ideas to solve the problems.

[151] Today, people all around the world celebrate Earth Day. It is a day to look at the Earth and see what needs to change. People talk about problems. Then, they try to solve them.

[185] Gaylord Nelson was one man with an idea. His idea grew into a worldwide celebration.

Adventure 4 • Lesson 3

# What Can I Do?

⭐ **D**o you want to help preserve our beautiful Earth? There are lots of things you can do. Recycling is an easy way to help. Most types of paper, like newspaper, magazines, cardboard, and even old mail, can be recycled. Don't just toss these things in the garbage. Set out a paper bag and fill it. Once a week, take the bag of old papers to be recycled. And don't forget about your old cans! These can be recycled too. Rinse out all the food or soda. Then, take them to be recycled when you take the paper.

★There are simple things you can do around the house too. Wash glass jars and lids and use them again. They're great for storing things. You can put leftovers in them. You can store small toys, buttons, and other things in them too.

★What do you do with old clothing? Some of it can go to friends or family. Sometimes clothes can't be worn anymore. Cut them into rags. Use those rags instead of paper towels. Then, use the rags to wash out jars.

★Look around your school. Schools use lots of paper each year. How can you cut back on the amount of paper used? Start a "Use It Up!" drive. Teach your classmates to use both sides of a sheet of paper. Make posters saying "Use the back, Jack!" and "Flip it over! Save a tree!"

★You can't just recycle, though. You need to buy recycled goods too. Next time you're shopping for paper, get recycled paper. Did you know many things are made from recycled plastic? Look closely at soda bottles, tables, bike racks, carpet, shoes, and some clothes. They can be made from recycled plastic. Buy recycled items whenever you can.

★Think of other things you can do, and then do them!

Adventure 4 • Lesson 4

# The Shrub

**E**ach day when Brandon and Darrell walked home from school, they stopped at the empty lot. They sat under a big bush and played games, talked, or just hung out. They called their special place "The Shrub." On Tuesday, they walked to the lot, but something was different.

A truck was parked on the lot. Two women and a man were unloading rakes, brooms, saws, and a lawn mower from the back of the truck.

"Hey, guys! My name's Gloria," said the tall woman. "Do you want to help us?"

"What are you doing?" asked Darrell.

Gloria explained that every day they drove by the empty lot and saw the overgrown trees, bushes, and trash. They decided the empty lot needed some attention. They were going to clean it and make it into a park.

"What are the saws for?" Brandon asked.

"We want to cut low branches off the trees and maybe cut down a few of these bushes," said one man.

"What about that big bush?" Brandon asked, pointing to the shrub.

"I like that one," said Gloria. "Maybe we'll just rake around it. It looks like a good place to sit."

"Give me a rake," said Darrell. "I'll start by cleaning around the big bush."

Soon, everyone was hard at work. Other people in the neighborhood stopped by to help. After two weeks of work, the lot began to look like a park. They made a stone path, cut back low branches, cleaned up trash, and cut back some bushes.

Darrell and Brandon ran to the park on the day the park benches arrived. No one could decide where the benches should go.

"I've got a place for one of them," said Brandon. He took one end of the bench and Darrell took the other. They carried the bench over to their special place—right under the shrub.

"That looks like the perfect place to play games, talk, or just hang out," Gloria said.

"It is," Darrell said. "Believe me, it is."

# The Pet Show

"**W**e're having a pet show on Friday," Ms. Ames said. "There will be prizes for cutest, best trick, tallest, smallest, quietest, and most unusual."

(24) Toby couldn't wait to show everyone at the neighborhood center his pet. He knew that no one else would have a pet like Stripes.

(48) On Friday, Toby gave Stripes a bath and brushed her hair. Before he put Stripes in her box, he pinned a bow in her hair.

(73) At the pet show, Ms. Ames asked the children to tell their pet's name and then walk their pet around the room so everyone could see.

(99) Tameesha had a fish in a tank. "This is Twinkles," she said. Twinkles swam in a circle.

(116) Kevin's dog, Max, walked on his back legs.

(124) Mia had a mouse in a cage. "This is Big Boy," she said laughing. Toby laughed because Big Boy was the smallest pet at the show.

(150) Toby walked to the middle of the room. When he took Stripes from her box, Mia screamed, and Tameesha held her nose. "Don't worry," Toby said. "She can't spray. This is Stripes, and she's a skunk who can't make a bad smell." Stripes held her head up high. Everyone clapped.

(200) Ms. Ames handed out the prizes, and of course, Tameesha won for quietest. Kevin won for best trick. Mia won for smallest. Toby also went home with a prize. Which prize do you think he won?

# Backyard Wildlife

"**I** wish the woods were not so far away," said Emma. "I wish I could live in a fairy tale where I could see animals every day."

"I have an idea," said her mother. "We have a little backyard, but we could make it a place for city wildlife. We can start with water. All animals need water for drinking or bathing."

On the first day, Emma and her mother set up a birdbath. They put a tub on the ground, and Emma filled it with water.

On the second day, birds were in the birdbath. Emma sat at the window and watched. The birds drank water and splashed together.

110 "If we had food for the birds, they might stay longer," Emma said. On the third day, Emma and her mother made a birdfeeder. They hung it on a pole.

Emma's job was to keep the birdbath clean. Once a week, she got a brush and scrubbed the tub. Then, she filled it with clean water. Her mother's job was to fill the feeder with birdseed and make sure the birdseed stayed dry.

One day, Emma's mother came home with a packet of seeds. She explained that they could plant the seeds and grow flowers. The flowers would attract butterflies and bees.

Soon, their backyard had birds, butterflies, bees, and one frog. Emma loved to sit at the window and watch the wildlife. It was better than living in a fairy tale.

# A Day for Trees

★**N**ebraska was once a plain with tall grasses and few trees. It was windy. Sometimes, the wind blew the soil away. In 1854, J. Sterling Morton moved from Detroit to Nebraska. He built a home and planted many trees around it.

**41** Morton was a writer. He worked for a newspaper. He wrote about the need for trees. In Nebraska, trees were needed to help stop the wind. They helped keep soil in place. They made shade from the hot summer sun.

**81** Morton thought there should be a holiday just for trees. He called it Arbor Day. On that day, people should plant trees. Prizes were given to towns that planted the largest number of trees. More than 1 million trees were planted in Nebraska on the first Arbor Day!

**129** Morton's birthday was April 22. That day became Arbor Day. Arbor Day is now celebrated in all 50 states. It is not always on April 22. The date depends on the best tree planting weather.

**164** There are many ways to celebrate Arbor Day. Bands play music about trees. Radio stations have contests. People answer hard questions about trees and win prizes. Schools have poster contests. Children make posters that tell how important trees are.

**203** The most important way to celebrate is to plant a tree.

# A Cat Worth Saving

★ The panther is the state mammal of Florida. A long time ago, panthers lived all over the eastern United States. Now, only 30 to 50 panthers are left in southern Florida. What happened to all the panthers?

★ People thought the panther was dangerous. They hunted it. Today, we know that panthers are not dangerous to people. They are very shy and stay away from places where people are. Panthers also hunt deer, wild hogs, and raccoons. Their hunting helps keep life in the wild balanced.

★ Today the panther is endangered. This means not many panthers are left, and we need to protect them. People in Florida can buy a special license plate for their cars. It has a picture of a panther on it. The money for the license plate goes to help protect the panther. The money is used to buy land. The land is set aside so that no one can build on it. It is land that wild animals can live on. Buying the plate is one way people in Florida can help save their state mammal.

# Holiday at City Park

**E**very year, I go with my family to Arbor Day at City Park. This year was different, though. This year, I was in the Arbor Day play. The play was the first event of Arbor Day this year, so I had to be at the park early. I was so excited about being in the play that I could hardly sleep. When my mom came in to wake me up, I was already up and dressed. I couldn't wait to get to the park!

In the play, a statue of J. Sterling Morton, the founder of Arbor Day, comes to life. I played the statue, and I told children how I came up with this holiday. I told all about trees and what happened on the first Arbor Day. At one part in the play, my friends Lin and Tomás were supposed to dig a hole to plant a tree. They walked onto the stage. Then, they walked to the pile of dirt. But Lin and Tomás just stood there. Then, I noticed that they forgot the shovel! When Lin started digging with her hands, it was hard to keep from laughing.

★ After the play, we went to hear my friend Rene's band. They played songs about trees. They played "King of Trees" and "Autumn Leaves." For fun, they sang "Seven Monkeys Up in a Tree." We had a great time.

At the end of Arbor Day, we learned about a paper drive that the Friends of the Park Club was planning. They said that every family could help. My family promised to bring our old newspapers to the park every week. I promised Dad I would help him bundle the papers. With the money they make from the paper drive, the club plans to plant a tree in City Park. I'm glad my family will be a part of such a special gift to the park.

# Cleaning the Mississippi River

Chad Predacke loves rivers. He grew up on the Mississippi River. He dived for clams there as a boy. When he grew up, he saw more and more trash along the river. In 1997, he decided to do something about it.

By himself, Chad cleaned more than 100 miles of the river. He picked up more than 22 tons of trash. The next year, Chad got help. Together with friends and volunteers, Chad cleaned more than 900 miles of the shore. He and his friends picked up and got rid of about 200 tons of trash.

⑨⑥ Chad has found trash of every shape and size. He has picked up bottles and cans. He has even found furniture in the water. He's picked up just about anything a person might throw away. Chad was asked to tell about a day cleaning the river. He said, "Days are like the river, always changing and always in motion with its high waters, low waters, fast waters, slow waters, windy waters, and calm waters. That's how my life is, always changing and on the move. It has given me the chance to explore where I am from. That has been the coolest thing about it."

How can one person make a difference? Chad saw a job that needed to be done, and he did it.